INSIDES,

OUT SIDES,

LOOPS

AND LINES

INSIDES, OUTSIDES, LOOPS AND LINES

by
Herbert Kohl

illustrated by **Winky Adam**

NOT JUST ANOTHER MATH BOOK

Scientific American
BOOKS FOR YOUNG READERS   W. H. FREEMAN AND COMPANY/ NEW YORK

I would like to acknowledge my editors at Scientific American Books for Young Readers, Nancy Laties Feresten and Marc Gave, for the time and effort they put into making this book a reality. In addition, two books were of great help as I organized the text: *Lusona: Geometrical Recreations of Africa* by Paulus Gerdes (African Mathematical Union, 1991, Maputo, Mozambique) and *Africa Counts* by Claudia Zaslavsky (Lawrence Hill Books, 1979, Brooklyn, New York). Finally I would like to acknowledge my wife, Judy, for her support and her unfailing humor and critical sensibility.

Scientific American Books for Young Readers is an imprint of
W. H. Freeman and Company, 41 Madison Avenue,
New York, New York 10010.

Book design by Debora Smith

Printed in the United States of America

10 9 8 7 6 5 4 3 2 1

ISBN 0-7167-6586-1

CONTENTS

INTRODUCTION

᧐ᕽ

Mysterious walled gardens with no entrances or exits . . .

Drawings that can be twisted and turned, shrunken and stretched, and still remain the same . . .

Patterns drawn on sand, dirt, or paper that start small and grow . . .

Strips of paper that can be twisted, taped, and cut to produced strange and surprising loops, twists, and twirls . . .

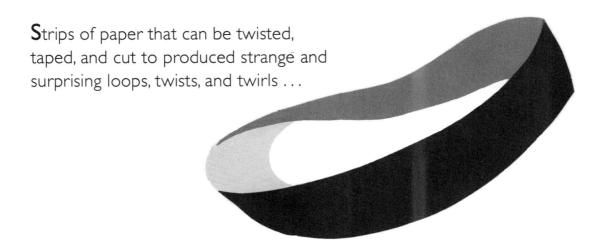

And maps to investigate with colored pencils and some clever thinking.

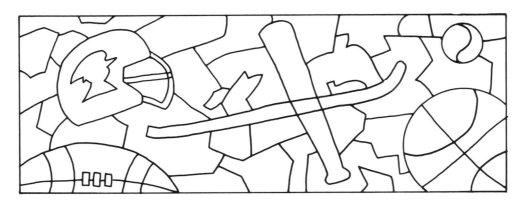

What do all of these things have in common? Well, they're all in this book. And they're all in this book because they're all math.

Mathematicians study patterns, both in nature and in the imagination. By fooling around with pencil and paper, they look for the ways patterns work just as you'll do in this book.

This is a write-in book. If it's yours, go ahead and write in the spaces provided. If you're borrowing the book from the library, put a piece of tracing paper over the page you're working on so you don't give the answer away to the next person. If you're using this book in school, your teacher can get permission to photocopy it. Ask him or her to look on the copyright page for information.

It's easiest to work through the book in order, doing each challenge as you come to it.

HAVE FUN!

CHAPTER 1
❧

Lost in the Garden:
Simple Closed Curves

We'll start out this book by investigating one of the most interesting shapes to a mathematician—a simple closed curve.

Simple closed curves are loops with no beginnings or ends and no crossings in them. Here are some examples of simple closed curves:

  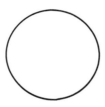 

Every simple closed curve divides the paper into one inside space and one outside space.

Color the inside of the simple closed curves on this page:

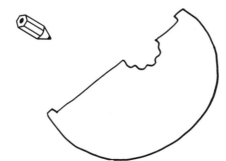 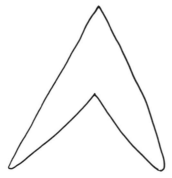 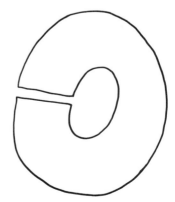

You can always tell that you've got a simple closed curve if you can color the figure without lifting your pencil, crossing a line, or spilling out of it.

Which of the figures on the page are simple closed curves? Color them in to find out. *

* The solutions to the challenges in this chapter are on pages 104–105, but don't turn to them until you've given yourself a chance.

Now try to identify some simple closed curves without coloring them. Just by looking, figure out which of these are simple closed curves.

For some simple closed curves, like the ones on this page, it is hard to find an inside and an outside.

Which of the points **A, B, C, D** and **E** are inside and which are outside the closed curve? Can you figure this out without coloring? Try, and then color in the drawing. Were you right?

Now try this one:

Figuring Out the Rules

Some simple closed curves are hard to color, either because they are very big or because they are very complicated. A mathematician named Camille Jordan looked for rules that would help him figure out whether a point was inside or outside a simple closed curve.

You can discover those same rules yourself.

CURVE **CHALLENGE 4**

A point inside a simple closed curve is like a person surrounded by a hedge.

Imagine you are inside a garden surrounded by a low hedge. The hedge creates a simple closed curve around you. If your friend is outside the hedge, you cannot meet unless one of you jumps over the hedge.

Now, what if the hedged-in garden was more complicated, like this one?

If you walked in a straight line, how many times would you have to jump the hedge to reach George outside the garden? (Try laying a straightedge from the dot near you to the dot near George. How many hedges does it cross?)

What if you were playing with the dog when you saw George coming? How many times would you have to jump the hedge then?

What if you were sitting at the table having a snack?

Here's that garden again.

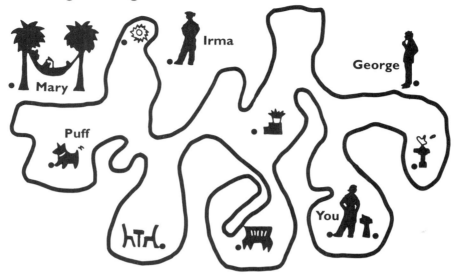

Count the number of times you would have to jump the hedge, and fill in this chart with the numbers. The first three lines are already filled in. (Remember to draw from dot to dot.)

Getting FROM **Inside** TO **Outside**—George

FROM	TO	NUMBER OF JUMPS
Sundial	George	3
Bench	George	5
Fountain	George	1
Steps	George	
Table	George	
Sunny spot	George	
Dog run	George	

What do you notice about all the numbers?

Now check your findings by using the other people outside the garden. Here's another chart. Fill it in with the number of times you'd need to jump the hedge to get from all the inside places to Mary, who is in the hammock, and to Irma, who is at the top of the garden

Getting FROM **Inside** TO **Outside**—Mary

FROM	TO	NUMBER OF JUMPS
Sundial	Mary	
Bench	Mary	
Fountain	Mary	
Steps	Mary	
Table	Mary	
Sunny spot	Mary	
Dog run	Mary	

Getting FROM **Inside** TO **Outside**—Irma

FROM	TO	NUMBER OF JUMPS
Sundial	Irma	
Bench	Irma	
Fountain	Irma	
Steps	Irma	
Table	Irma	
Sunny spot	Irma	
Dog run	Irma	

Are the numbers in the new charts similar in any way to those in your first chart?

Use this page to continue the experiment by drawing your own simple-closed-curve garden. Make it as complicated or as simple as you want, but remember: A simple closed curve is a single loop that has no beginning and no end, and that can be colored in without lifting your pencil, crossing a line, or spilling out.

Make some charts of the number of times the hedge must be jumped to get from an inside point to an outside point.

FROM	TO	NUMBER OF JUMPS

FROM	TO	NUMBER OF JUMPS

What do you now know about the number of times you must cross the hedge when you travel from inside to outside a simple closed curve?

Now we'll take a look at another kind of path, one that goes from one outside point to another.

Here's another simple-closed-curve garden.

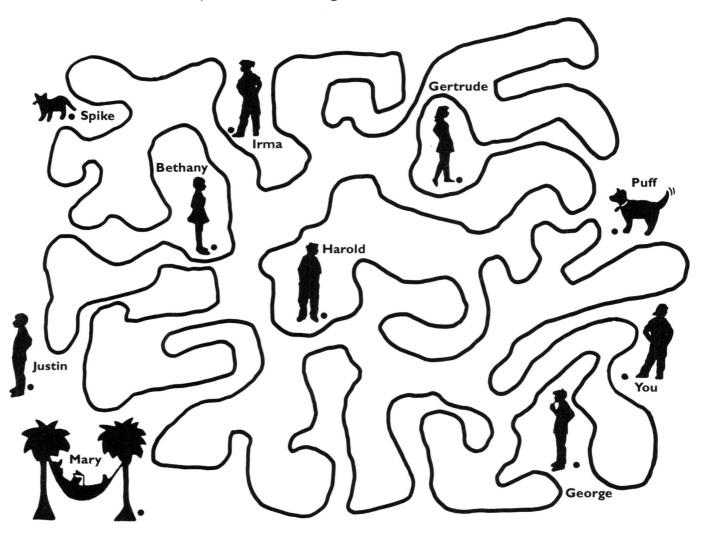

You are outside the garden and are trying to reach your guests. Although you are all outside the garden, sections of the hedge come between you. Rather than finding your way around the hedge to meet your friends, you decide to take the shortest route—a straight line—and jump over.

How many times will you have to jump the hedge to meet each friend?

The best way to think through this problem is to make another chart:

Traveling FROM **Outside** TO **Outside**

FROM	TO	NUMBER OF JUMPS
You	George	2
You	Mary	10
You	Irma	8
You	Bethany	
You	Justin	
You	Harold	
You	Gertrude	
You	Spike	
You	Puff	

Compare this chart with the charts you made for traveling from inside to outside. What is the difference between the kind of numbers you get when you go from inside to outside and the kind of numbers you get when you go from outside to outside?

What rules did you discover?

Now, say you find yourself in the midst of one of these simple-closed-curve gardens, but it is so complicated that you can't tell whether you are inside the ring of hedge or outside it.

Luckily, you glance up and see that Spike is coming down the road toward you. He is definitely outside the hedge. If you know that Spike is outside, how would you figure out whether you are outside or inside?

Try counting jumps.

How many times do you have to jump over the hedge to reach Spike?

What does the number tell you?

Imagine yourself in another position in the garden. Now how many hedges do you have to jump to get to Spike?

Did you start inside the hedge or outside it this time?

CURVE **CHALLENGE 10**

Try another complicated curve:

This time, draw your own outside point and test other, unknown points.

Now draw a new simple closed curve and try some more points.

Does the method you discovered work?

Beginning with sketches, lists, and lots of fiddling around, you have come to discover a general statement that holds for an infinite number of possible drawings (or simple-closed-curve gardens). This movement from sketch and idea to general statement or rule is a good example of how mathematicians work.

The rule you have just discovered is called Jordan's Inside-Outside Theorem. Mathematicians state it like this: Beginning with an outside point, draw a line to a second point x. If you cross an odd number of boundaries, the point x is inside the curve. If you cross an even number of boundaries, the point x is outside the curve.

This method was first explored by the French mathematician Camille Jordan (1838–1922).

It's interesting that Jordan's own proof of the theorem named after him turned out to be wrong. He guessed right about the answer, but he didn't succeed in writing out a logical proof of it that other mathematicians agreed upon. Many years passed before someone came up with a simple proof of the theorem. It is interesting that turning a true mathematical insight into a proof can be such a difficult challenge. It shows that having mathematical ideas and writing them down in ways that convince other people they are true are not the same thing.

CHAPTER 2

❧

Map Coloring:
Figuring Out the Rules

On any political map of the world, it is possible to trace national boundaries. On a map of North America, you can easily find the borders of Canada, the United States, and Mexico, for example.

All maps that can be drawn on a flat piece of paper are made up of simple closed curves like the ones we explored in the last chapter.

Mapmakers color complicated maps in order to distinguish different countries. Mathematicians who are looking for the rules that govern simple closed curves study the nature of all possible map colorings. The question for mathematicians is: What is the smallest number of colors you can use to color a map?

In math there are different types of maps. The first maps we will work with are very simple. Then we'll consider more complicated maps. The main coloring rule in all of these maps is the same. It is:

 When you color a mathematical map, no two areas that touch each other (that is, that have a common boundary) can be the same color. There is one exception: Areas that touch *at only one point* can be the same color.

Allowed to be same color:

Not allowed to be same color:

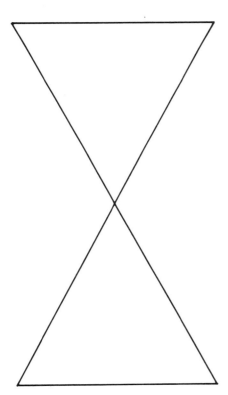

MAP **CHALLENGE** I

On page 27 draw a line from any edge to any other edge. The line may start and finish at any point along any edge, but it may not cross itself. *

Your page might look like this: Or this:

Or this: Or this:

As you can see, the line does not need to be straight or smooth. How many colors will you need to color your map, using these rules?

▶ **Use the fewest possible colors.**

▶ **Countries that share a border must be different colors.**

▶ **Countries that meet at a point or that don't share a border may be the same color.**

Here are the maps on this page, with colors added, to give you the idea:

* The solutions to the challenges in this chapter are on pages 106–109, but don't turn to them until you've given yourself a chance.

Now, on page 29 draw two lines that begin and end on the edges of the paper. The lines don't have to be straight, and they may cross each other; but they may not overlap.

Your map might look like this: Or this:

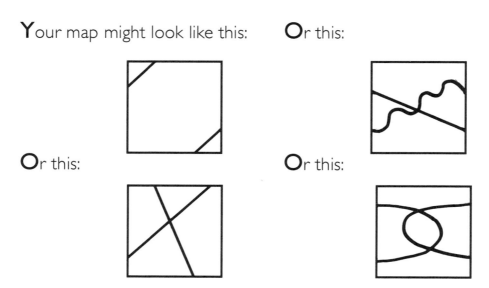

Or this: Or this:

Or it may look like none of these. As long as it's made of two lines running from an edge to an edge, it's right. That's because we're trying to find out how many colors we'll need to color any map made with lines that run edge to edge. The more different maps you can come up with that have lines running edge to edge, the better you can experiment.

Use your own paper to make several more maps with two lines running edge to edge.

How many colors do you need to color your two-line maps? Here are the ones on this page to give you an idea:

   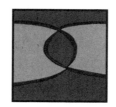

Now, on page 31 draw any number of lines from edge to edge. Again, lines may cross but not overlap. Color this new map.

Your map might look like this: **O**r this:

Or this: **O**r this:

   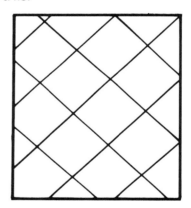

Yours might be even more complicated. After all, you have more space.

How many colors do you need for your very complicated, many-lined maps?

Did you find that all the maps you made by drawing lines from edge to edge can be colored with two colors? This is a mathematical discovery.

Maps with Simple Closed Curves

Now that you've worked out the coloring rule for maps made of lines that cross a piece of paper from edge to edge, let's try something new. In this section, we'll explore maps that are made of simple closed curves, standing alone and overlapping. As we saw in Chapter 1, simple closed curves have no beginning point or end point. Here are some examples:

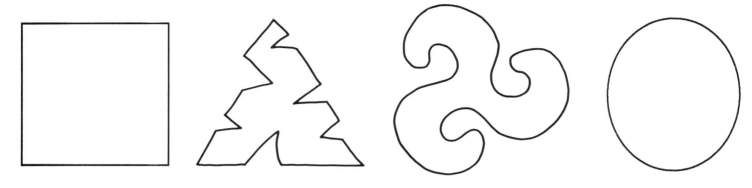

A simple closed curve divides a page into two parts: an inside and an outside.

MAP **CHALLENGE 4**

Color in the map on page 33.

Remember the rules:

▶ Use as few colors as you can.
▶ No two areas that share a boundary may be the same color.
▶ Areas that meet at a point may be the same color.

How many colors do you need to color a map with one simple closed curve?

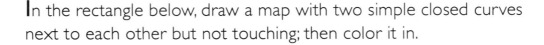

In the rectangle below, draw a map with two simple closed curves next to each other but not touching; then color it in.

Your map might look like this: Or this:

Or this: Or this:

How many colors do you need to color your map and the others on this page? (Remember, you are trying to find the fewest colors you can use.) Here's one colored for you:

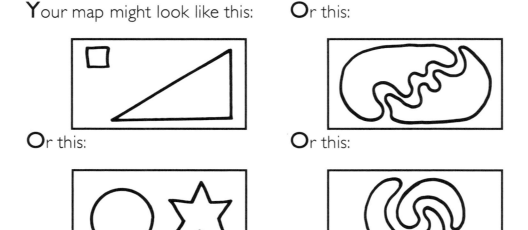

In this rectangle, draw a map with two simple closed curves that cross each other but don't share a boundary. Note: The part of one curve that overlaps the other curve becomes a new curve with its own boundaries, like this:

Your map might look like this: Or this:

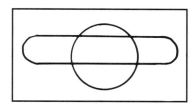

Or this: Or this:

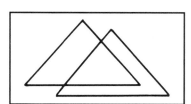

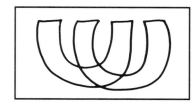

How many colors do you need to color a map with two simple closed curves that cross but don't share a boundary?

Now, use these rectangles to make maps that use simple closed curves, standing alone and overlapping. Make your maps as complicated or simple as you want, following these rules:

▶ The maps must be made of simple closed curves only.

▶ The simple closed curves may cross each other.

▶ The simple closed curves may *not* share a boundary.

The first one is done for you.

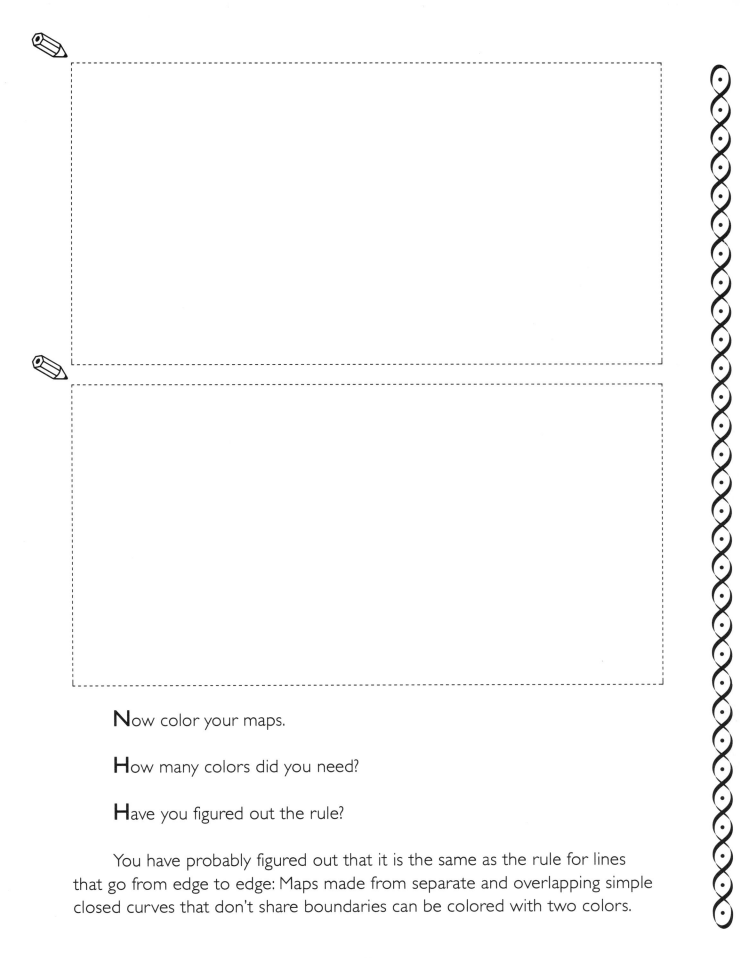

Now color your maps.

How many colors did you need?

Have you figured out the rule?

You have probably figured out that it is the same as the rule for lines that go from edge to edge: Maps made from separate and overlapping simple closed curves that don't share boundaries can be colored with two colors.

Maps with Edge-to-Edge Lines and Simple Closed Curves

With each challenge, you have discovered more kinds of maps. Let's combine the two kinds of maps that need only two colors: those made of lines that go from edge to edge, and those made of simple closed curves that cross but don't share boundaries.

MAP **CHALLENGE 8**

Create several maps that combine simple closed curves and lines that go from edge to edge. We've done one to get you started.

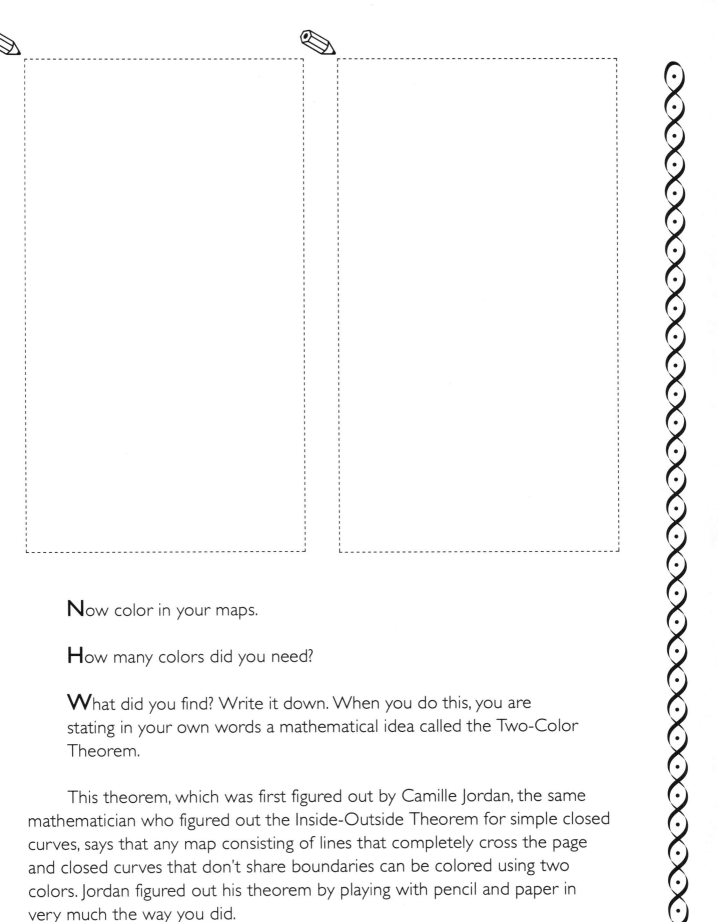

Now color in your maps.

How many colors did you need?

What did you find? Write it down. When you do this, you are stating in your own words a mathematical idea called the Two-Color Theorem.

This theorem, which was first figured out by Camille Jordan, the same mathematician who figured out the Inside-Outside Theorem for simple closed curves, says that any map consisting of lines that completely cross the page and closed curves that don't share boundaries can be colored using two colors. Jordan figured out his theorem by playing with pencil and paper in very much the way you did.

All Maps That Can Be Drawn on a Flat Piece of Paper

So far you have investigated maps made with lines that run edge to edge and simple closed curves. The simple closed curves either didn't touch each other or overlapped without sharing boundaries. You have figured out that these maps can all be colored with two colors. But most maps in the real world include lines that don't cross the entire paper. Often they come together to make simple closed curves that share boundaries. These maps need more than two colors.

MAP **CHALLENGE 9**

This drawing shows three islands.

Which of these islands follows the two-color rule?

Try coloring in the islands.

Remember the map-coloring rules:

- ▶ Use as few colors as possible.
- ▶ No two areas that share a border may be the same color.
- ▶ Areas that meet at a point may be the same color.

How many colors do you need to color Tiny Island?

How many for Narrow Island?

How many for Triangle Island?

MAP **CHALLENGE 10**

Here are some more maps.

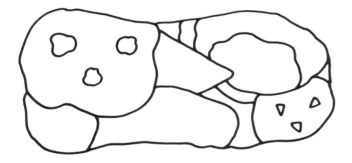 

Color them.

How many colors did you need to color each one?

One way to figure out how many colors a map will need even without coloring it is to find its pattern.

Let's take a look at those islands again.

The map of Tiny Island is like the first maps we looked at in Challenge 1. It's a space with a line running from edge to edge. You can color Tiny Island with two colors.

The map of Narrow Island is different from any map we've seen so far. Each country borders the other two. As you have discovered, you need three colors to color Narrow Island.

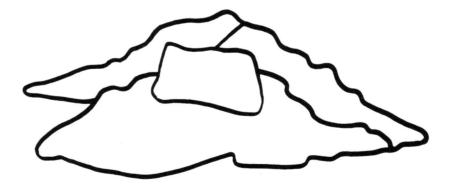

On the map of Triangle Island there is a country surrounded by three other countries that all border one another. That is different from Tiny Island and Narrow Island. When you experimented, did you find that it took four colors to color Triangle Island?

Now look at this map:

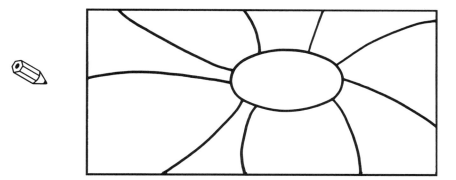

Guess how many colors you would need to color it. Color it in and see if you guessed fight.

Now try this one:

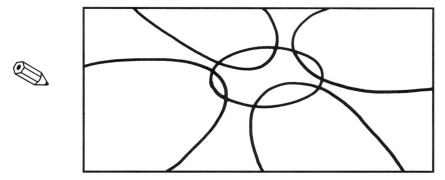

And this one:

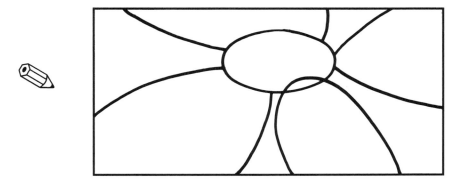

How many colors does each map need?

Try drawing your own maps.

Start with a map that can be colored with only two colors.
(Remember the Two-Color Theorem from page 39?)

Now draw a map that needs three colors.

Now one that needs four colors:

Try another three-color map:

And another four-color map:

What rules are you using when you draw your maps?

MAP **CHALLENGE 13**

Here are some maps of different parts of the world.

Here is a map of the Yucatán Peninsula in southern Mexico and some nearby countries in Central America.

What is the smallest number of colors you need to color this map?

Here's one of Australia. How many colors do you need?

Here are southwestern Canada and the northwestern United States.

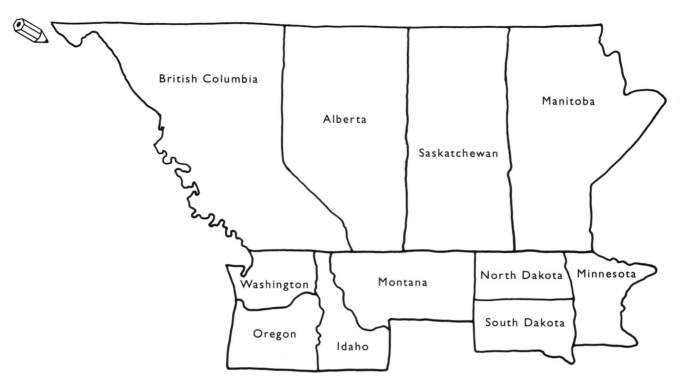

This map shows southern Africa.

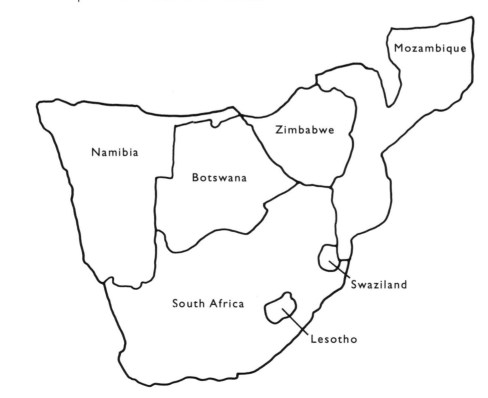

Map Games

Here are some map games that can be played by any number of people using any size sheet of paper. Get a friend and try these games using our game boards; then make some of your own and throw a party.

THE BOARD

Each game board is a mathematical map like the ones you've been working with in this chapter.

THE PLAYERS

The two-color game can be played by any even number of players divided into two teams.

The Big Rule:

> ▸ **No two countries that share a border may be the same color (though two countries of the same color may touch at a point).**

THE PLAY

1. Each team chooses a color.

2. Flip a coin to decide which team goes first.

3. A player from the first team colors a single country with his or her color.

4. A player from the second team colors a country using his or her color.

5. The teams take turns until one team cannot color in any country.

6. The team that colors the last country wins.

What makes the game interesting is that as it goes on, some countries cannot be colored in by either team, because they share borders with countries of two different colors—like this:

Find a worthy opponent, and finish up this game. It's the lighter color team's turn.

And this one:

And this one:

VARIATION 1—MAKING THE GAME BOARD

Make your own game boards. Creating the board can be part of the game:

1. One player draws a shape anywhere on the paper.

2. The next player draws another shape.

3. The players take turns drawing shapes. Make your shapes small if you want your game to take a long time and big if you want it to take a short time. The map might look something like this:

Now you have a game board. Play on it.

Use this page to make your own game board.

VARIATION 2—GAMES WITH THREE OR FOUR COLORS

In these variations, three or four players each choose a different color and take turns.

Use the board you created on page 56 for a three-color game.

Create a new board below for a four-color game.

CHAPTER 3

ℰℛ

Tracings:

Simple Beginnings Lead to Complicated Patterns

Sometimes very simple ideas can lead to complicated and unexpected discoveries. Just doodling around with pencil and paper, drawing and enlarging simple patterns, then thinking about your results can get you involved in doing mathematics without knowing it. Here's a simple challenge to get you started.

TRACING **CHALLENGE 1**

Take a pencil and trace over each diagram, beginning at the spot labeled **START HERE**. These are the rules:

- ▶ You must trace over all lines of the diagram.
- ▶ You may not pick up your pencil while tracing.
- ▶ You may not trace over a line that you have already traced.

START HERE →

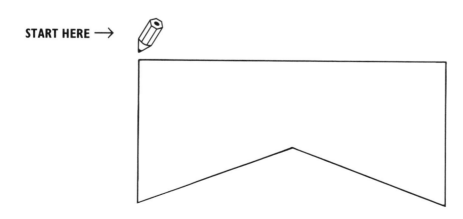

58

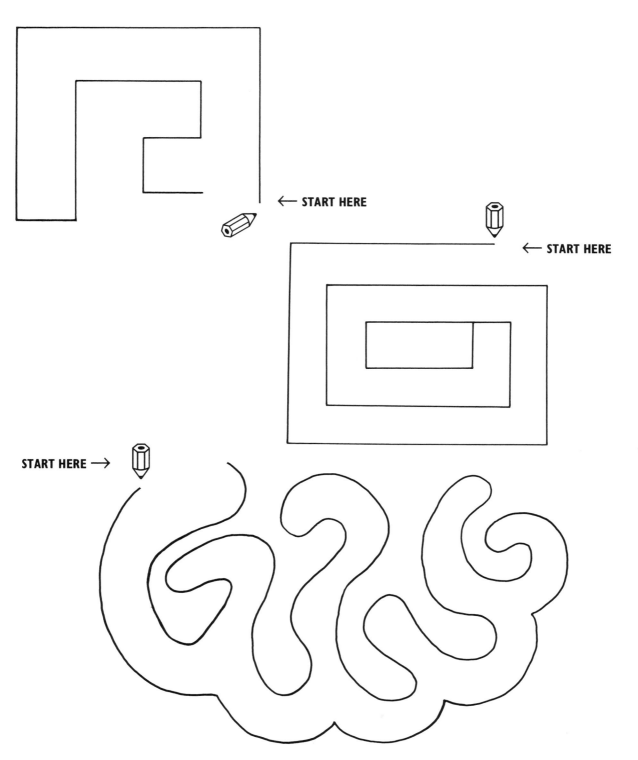

← **START HERE**

← **START HERE**

START HERE →

Now that you have the idea, these four diagrams may seem pretty easy to trace. All you needed to do was put your pencil down at the beginning and follow along the line. Any route you chose would trace the entire figure without tracing over any line you had already drawn.

Here is a more difficult tracing challenge.*

Begin at any point on this diagram and trace it, using the same rules as before.

❱ **Your lines may touch at a corner or cross but not overlap.**

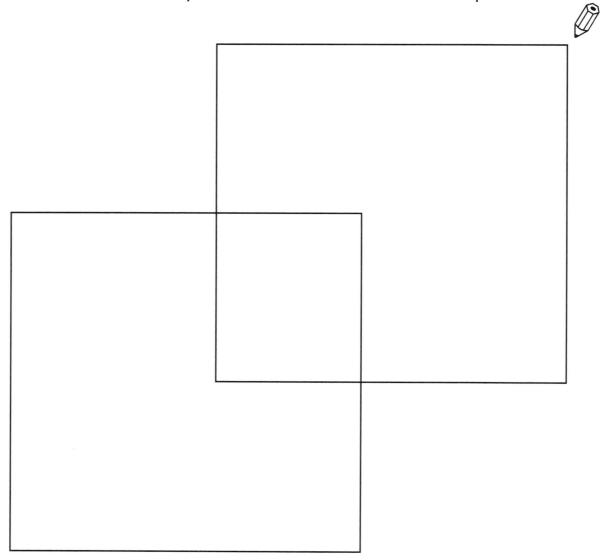

---

* You can find the solutions to the puzzles in this chapter on pages 110–112. But give yourself a chance to find the solutions before you peek.

Now use the method you figured out when you were tracing the diagram on the left to trace these two drawings.

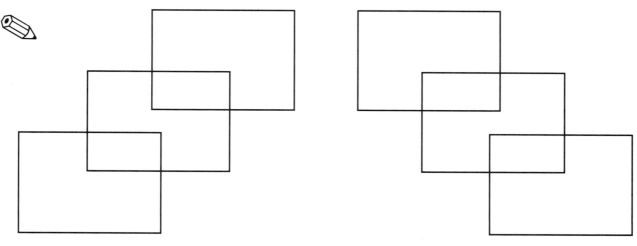

And these:

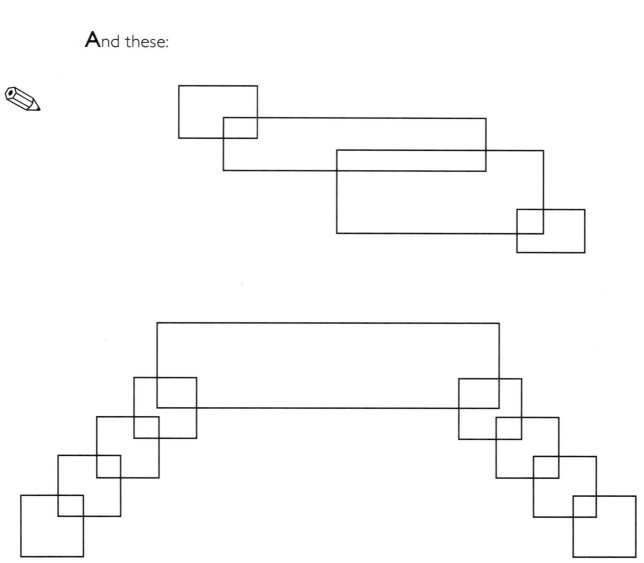

Lusona

Drawing complex patterns is a tradition of the Tchokwe people, who live in northeast Angola, in southern Africa. The Tchokwe people and their neighbors are famous for the designs they create on baskets, mats, rugs, paintings, tattoos, and the walls of their homes.

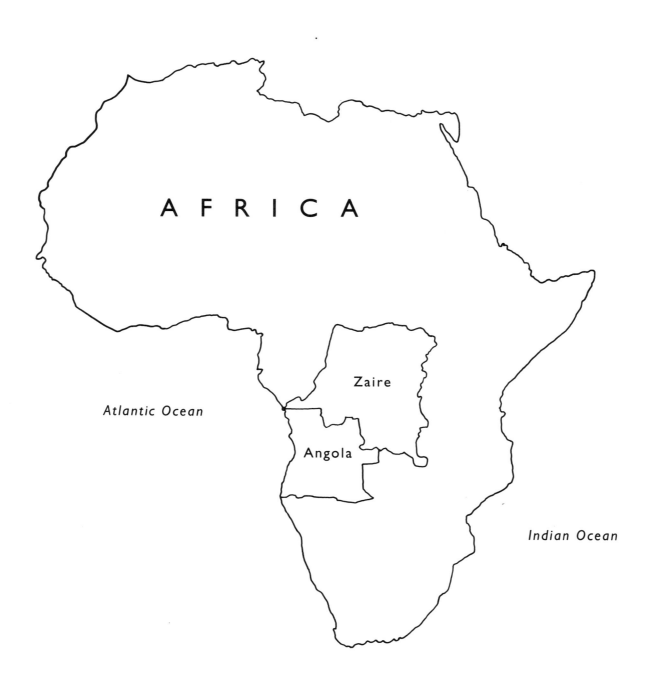

Patterns drawn on the ground in sand or dirt are particularly important in Tchokwe culture. Tchokwes call these drawings *lusona*. Here are two examples:

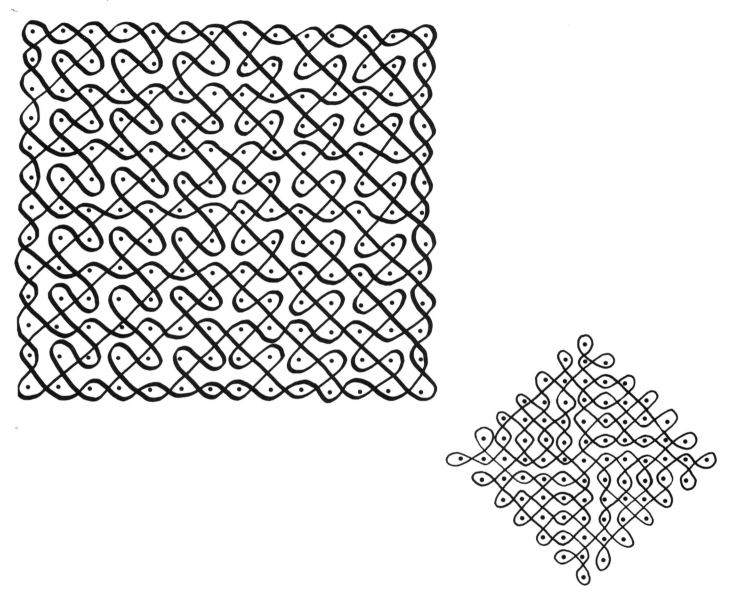

Traditionally, when the Tchokwe people meet in village squares or at hunting sites, specialists called *akwa kuta sona* ("those who know how to draw") make these complicated patterns. The patterns illustrate stories, proverbs, tools, the natural environment, and community history. The simpler patterns are turned into riddles and puzzles. These lusona are not straight-forward illustrations of the Tchokwe people's surroundings. They are patterns that follow a set of rules but that also represent objects.

To draw a lusona, the *akwa kuta sona* first smooths out the sand or dirt and makes a grid of points with his fingertips. He then uses the grid as a guide and draws the traditional pattern.

Here is a simple four-point grid that the *akwa kuta sona* would use to guide his drawing of a single kumbi bird, a kind of stork. Next to it is the finished drawing.

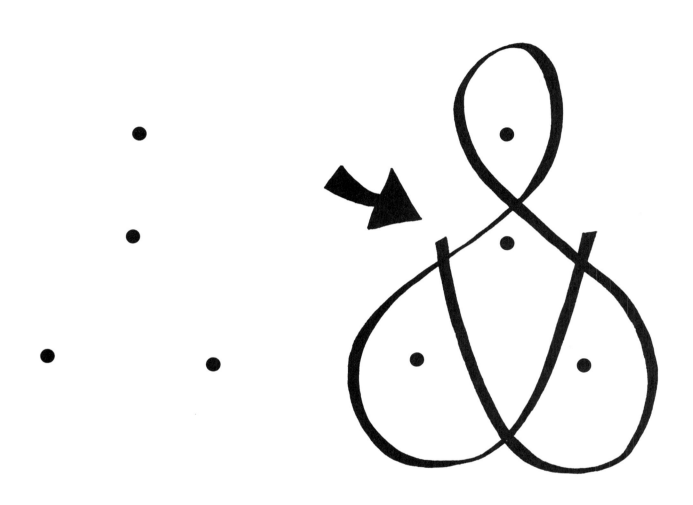

The rules for drawing lusona are the same as those you followed when you did tracings.

- ▶ **You must draw the bird without lifting your pencil.**
- ▶ **You may not retrace a line you have already drawn.**

Lusona Practice

To get the idea, use your pencil to trace these drawings, completing the unfinished ones.

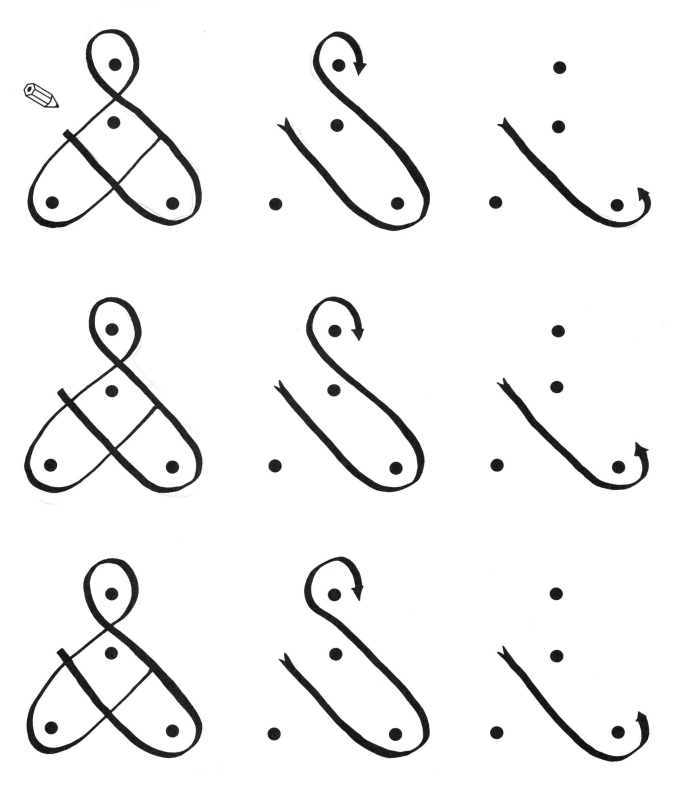

Here is a page of grids.

Use each grid as a guide for drawing a kumbi bird like the one on page 64. Draw the kumbi over and over until you can do it from the grid, without looking at the completed picture.

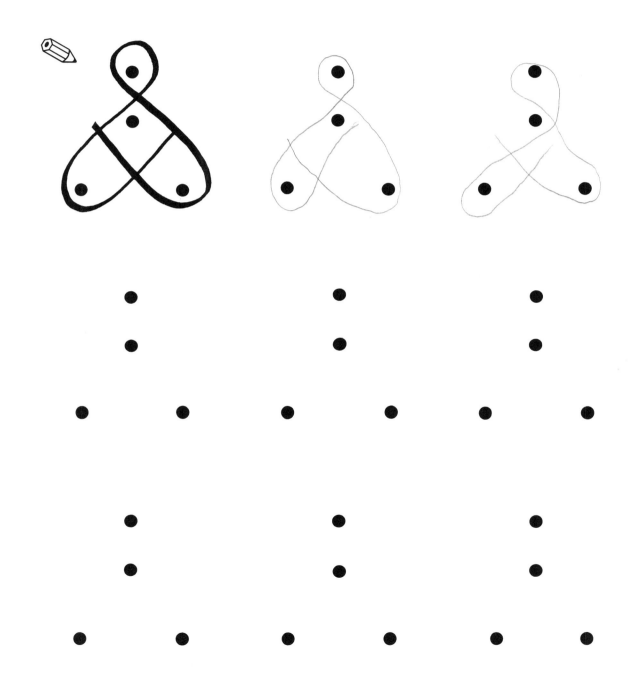

Here is the lusona of a family of three kumbi birds:

Use the grid below and practice drawing the three-bird lusona.

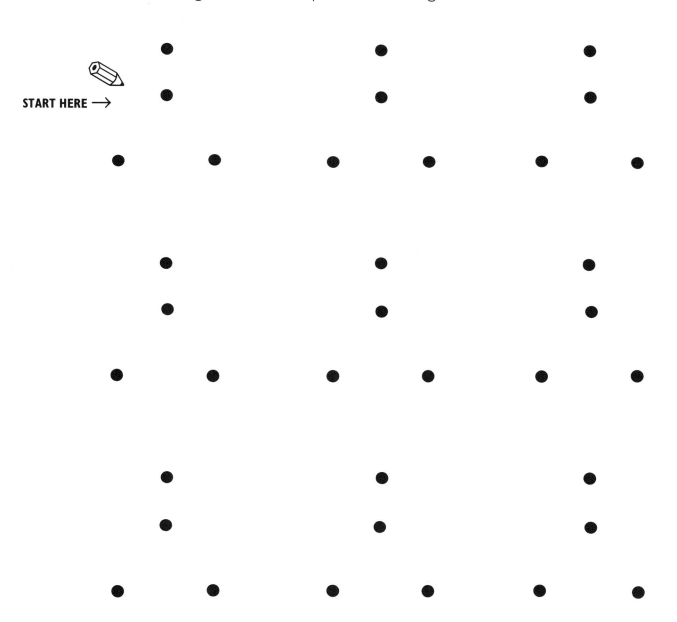

START HERE →

Add a few more birds and practice until you can draw them smoothly and easily.

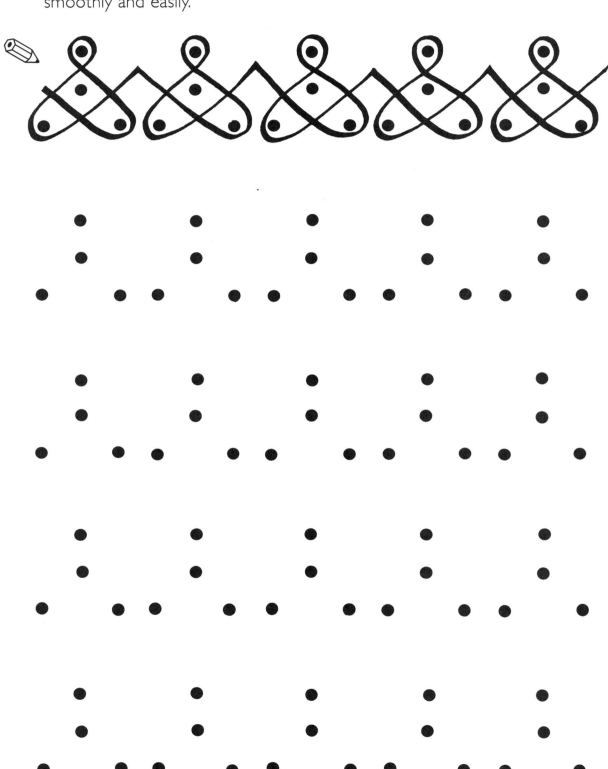

Now try drawing the flock of kumbi birds.

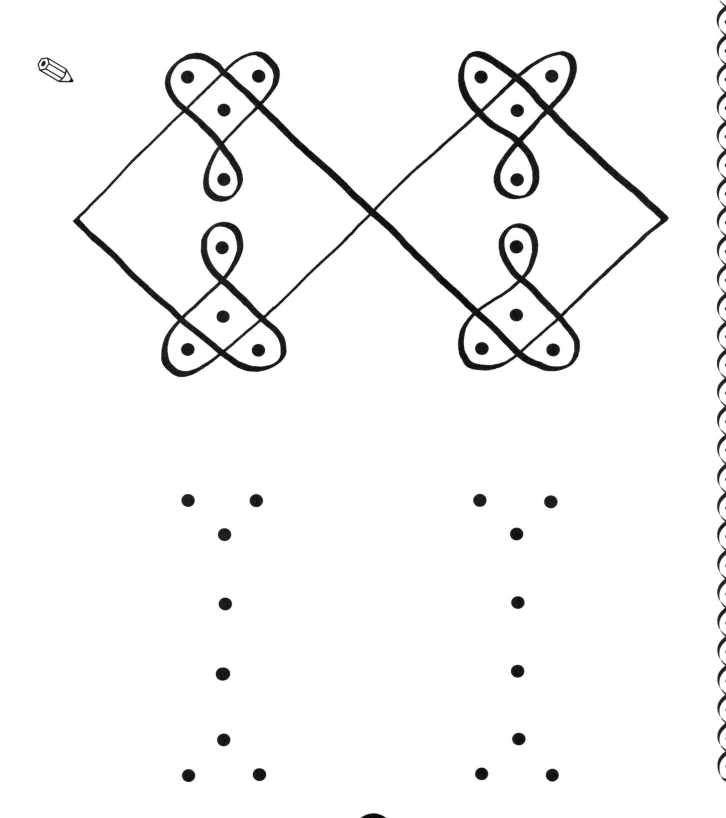

Try this more complicated pattern unit, the flying bird. Practice drawing until it's easy for you.

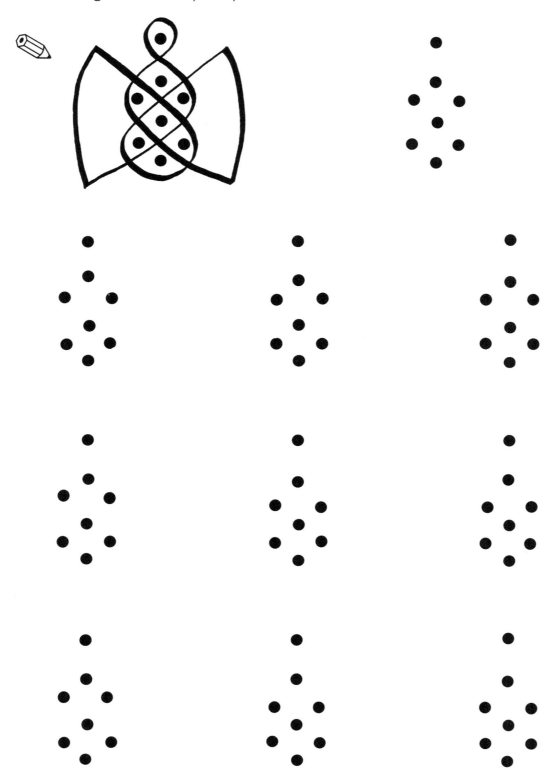

Now use what you have learned to draw these birds flying together.

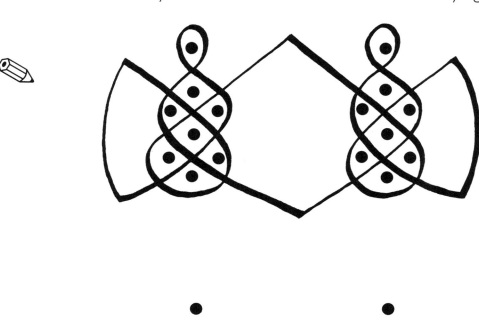

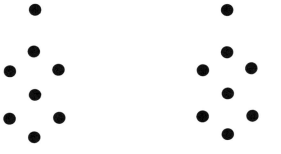

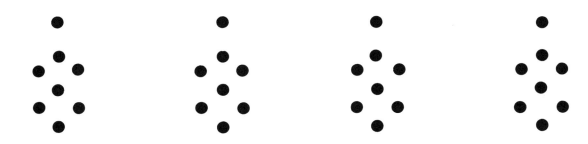

Use the same ideas to work on this very complicated three-bird formation.

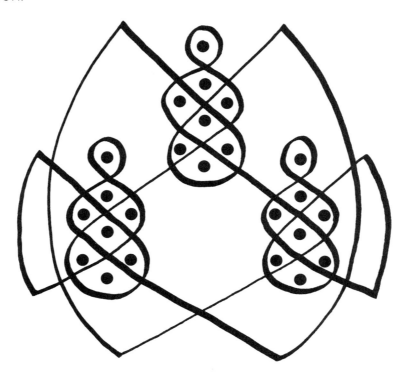

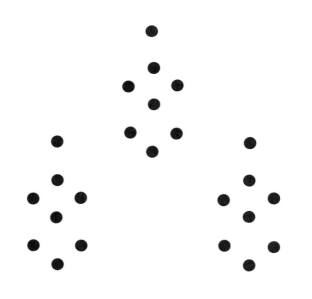

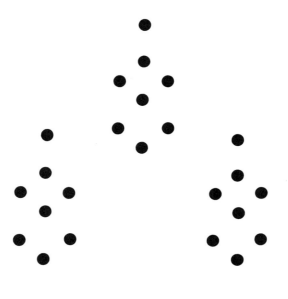

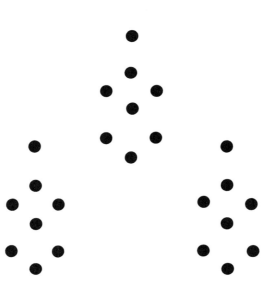

Try a scorpion.

Try a nest of scorpions.

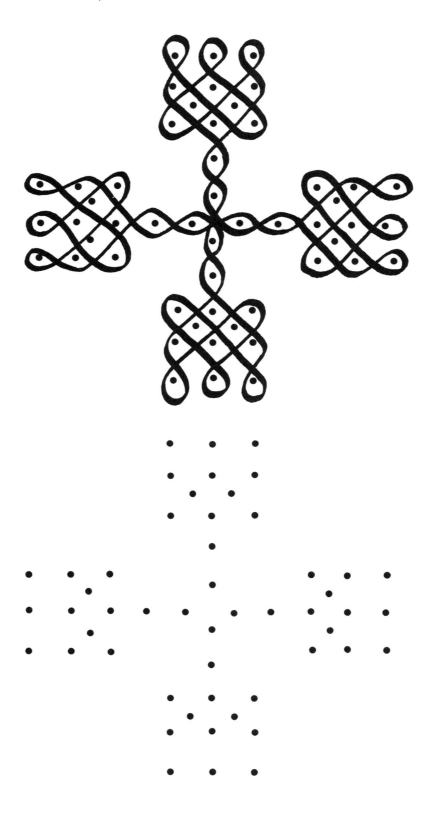

The *akwa kuta sona* draw the patterns you have worked on and many more. All of these lusona are small units and the complex patterns based on them. Here is how a large pattern is developed from a smaller unit.

First a small figure is created.

Then the figure is expanded . . .

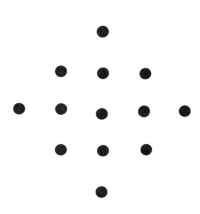

more . . .

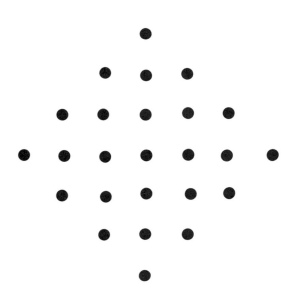

and more.

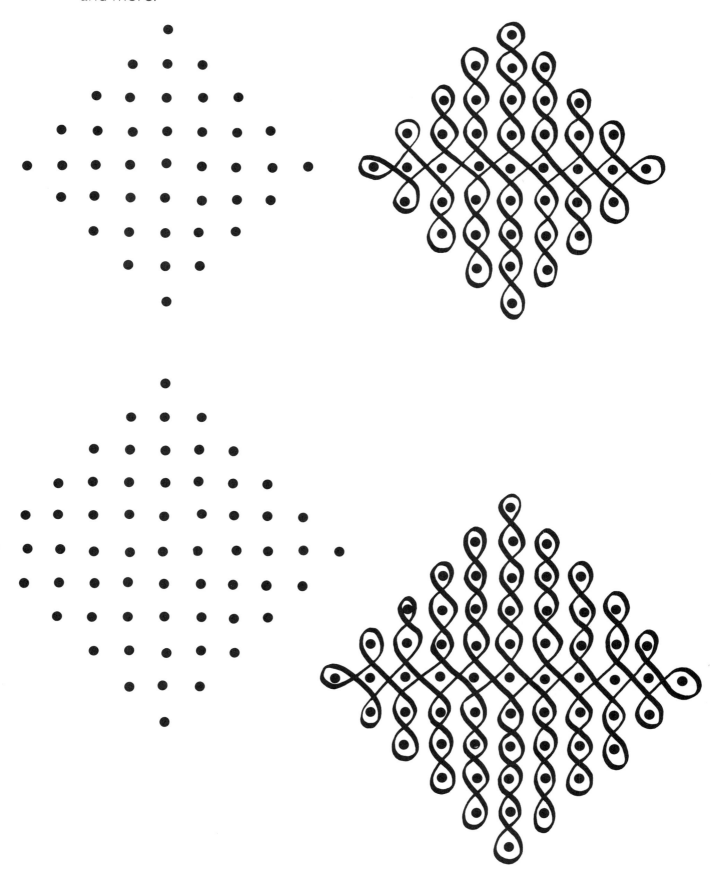

Try to make up some lusona yourself. Begin with a simple one.

Then make that simple lusona more complex. Start by expanding the grid. Then draw the larger lusona around the expanded grid. Practice until you can feel the pattern that makes up the design and do the drawing with ease.

Here are three lusona that tell a bit about the daily life of the Tchokwe.
Study the patterns, and they might give you some ideas for your own lusona.

a village protected by a fence

a stick to carry dried fish

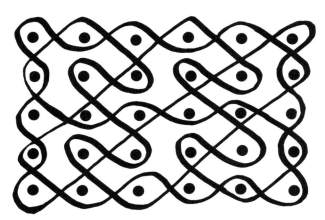

the path of a chicken being chased

Finding a Starting Point

Some figures, such as the lusona, are made of a single line. They can be traced starting at the end if they are open or starting anywhere if they are closed.

But some figures are not so easily traced. Some can't be traced without either lifting the pencil from the paper or doubling over a line.

Here is a figure. Use a colored pencil to trace over it beginning at the starting point.

Don't forget the rules:

▶ You must trace over all lines of the diagram.

▶ You may not pick up your pencil while tracing.

▶ You may not trace over a line that you have already traced.

START HERE →

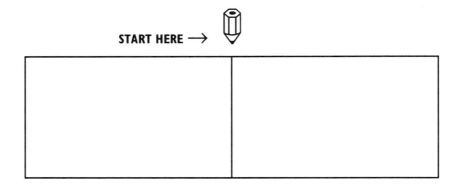

Now trace the same figure beginning at another starting point. Can you do it in one continuous line without picking up your pencil or retracing?

START HERE →

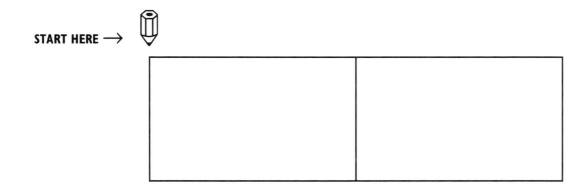

It is not possible to trace this figure from this starting point with one continuous line. All possible ways lead to traps that make the tracing impossible. Often whether or not you can trace a figure depends on the starting point you choose. When you try to trace a figure, it is important not to give up too early. You may have begun at the wrong point.

TRACING **CHALLENGE 13**

Here is one figure repeated three times. Trace it beginning at the three starting points marked.

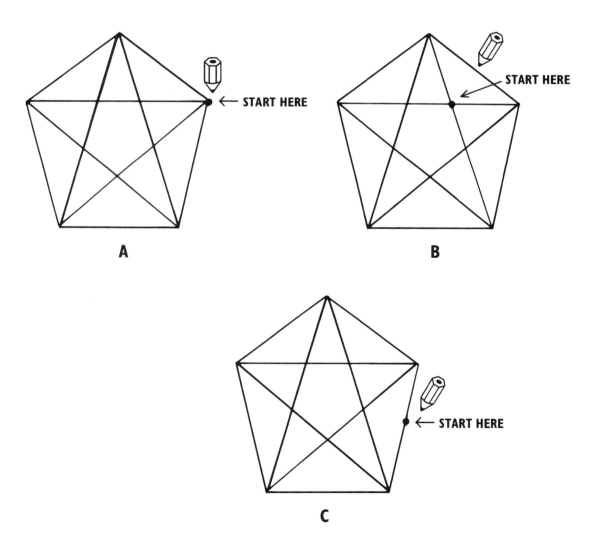

← START HERE

A

START HERE

B

← START HERE

C

How did your starting point change the way you traced the figure?

Here's another figure to try. Trace from the marked starting points.

Which work? Which don't? You may want to make some extra copies on your own paper so you can try lots of variations.

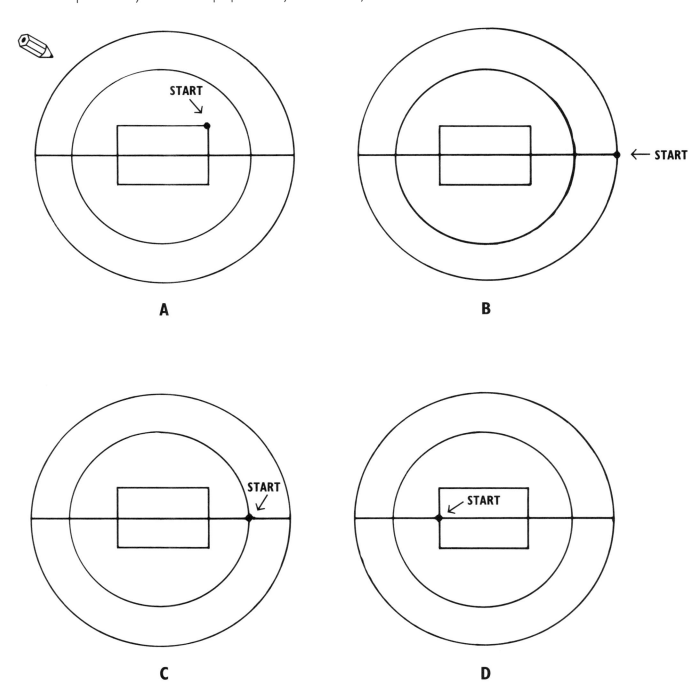

A

B

C

D

We've seen that some figures can be traced from any point, that some can be traced from one or several points. But there are some figures that can't be traced by the rules at all, from any point.

As a final tracing challenge, figure out which of the following figures can be traced. Which can't?

You may want to copy them onto your own paper so you can try lots of different approaches.

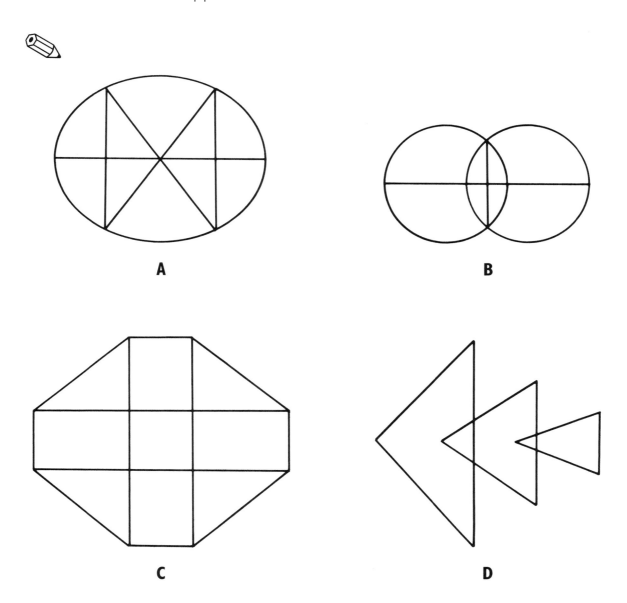

A

B

C

D

CHAPTER 4

Stretching, Bending, and Twisting:
A New Way of Looking at Shapes

Mathematicians look at patterns in many different ways. They look for repetition of shapes, the way we did with lusona. They look for the rules that govern relations among shapes, the way we did with maps. They also look at boundaries: what is inside and outside them, and what crosses them. The study of boundaries is called *topology*. When you are thinking topologically, two shapes that look very different can be exactly the same.

Imagine you have a piece of paper made of a special kind of material that can be stretched or shrunk into any size or shape no matter how big or small. Next imagine drawing a simple face somewhere on the sheet.

Without drawing any new lines or erasing old ones but simply by twisting, stretching, shrinking, bending, and expanding your sheet, you can change your drawing. For example, by stretching, you can turn your original face into this one:

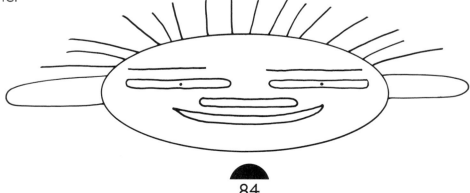

You can make even more complicated changes by pulling and twisting and shrinking and pulling again.

Begin with the original drawing:

If you stretch the face sideways, you get this:

If you then make the eyes different sizes and shapes and put these on the same side of the face, you get this:

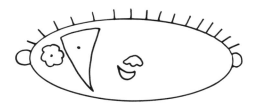

If you stretch and squiggle the nose and move the mouth over, you get this:

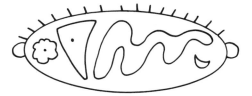

If you move the ears to the bottom of the face and stretch them out, you get this:

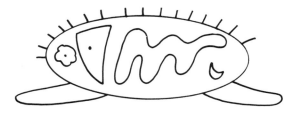

Notice that no matter how much you stretch or shrink or move things around in the face, some things about it remain unchanged. The eyes, nose, and mouth stay within the outline, or boundary, of the face. The eyeballs stay inside the eyes, and the ears remain attached to and outside the outline of the face.

All the versions of the face on the previous page are topologically equivalent. That means each face can be twisted, stretched, shrunk, bent, or expanded until it looks like the others. Here's a shape:

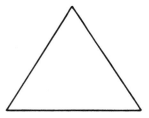

We know it as a triangle, but the important thing about it topologically is that it has one inside and one outside. It is a simple closed curve.

Using that flexible sheet to twist and stretch it, we can turn it into this shape:

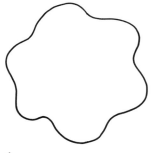

And this shape:

And this shape:

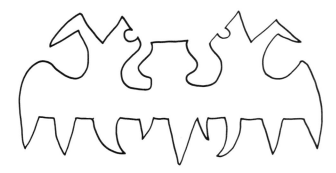

Each of the shapes on this page has one inside and one outside. They are topologically equivalent.

Here are some topologically equivalent pairs of drawings. Take a close look at them and figure out how one can be twisted into the other. (One way to figure this out is to imagine an animated cartoon that shows the drawings changing into one another.)

 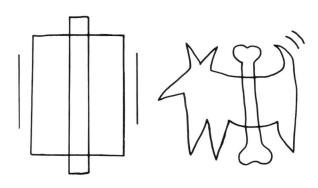

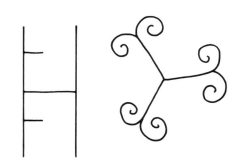 

 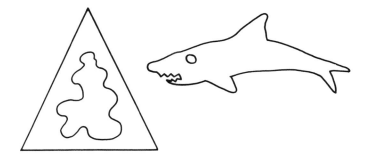

Here are some pairs of drawings. Circle the pairs that are topologically equivalent. One is already done for you.

What is the same about the pairs that are topologically equivalent?

What is different about the ones that are topologically different?

In each of these groups of drawings, one drawing is topologically different from the others.

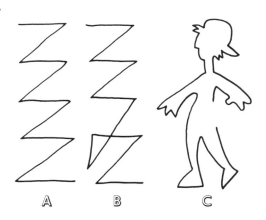

3.

Which drawing is topologically different?

In each group, what makes the two topologically equivalent drawings alike?

In each group, what makes the other drawing different?

Writing down the characteristics of the group of figures that are the same will help you to understand what mathematicians think about when they do topology.

Here are some more difficult challenges to play with. In each example, one of the figures to the right is topologically different from the figure on the left.

In each set, circle the drawing on the right that is topologically different from the drawing on the left. What makes it different?

1.

   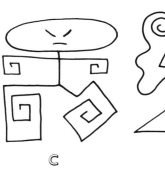 

A   B   C   D

2.

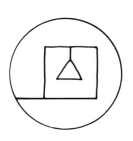  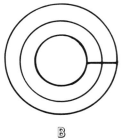 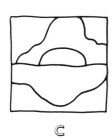 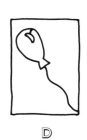

A   B   C   D

3.

A   B   C   D

4.

A   B   C   D

5.

A   B   C   D

The Topology of Alphabets

People give meaning to shapes. When English speakers see the letters S L I M, they know from the shapes of the letters and their order what the word means. When the Chinese see the character 魚 , they know that it means "fish."

But as we have just seen, there are other ways to look at shapes. Look at the letters S L I M from a topological point of view.

Imagine pulling at the ends of these letters. Each of them can be unbent into a straight line. They are topologically equivalent.

DISTORTION **CHALLENGE 5**

Here is the English alphabet.

 ABCDE FGH IJ KLMNOPQRSTUVWXYZ

Circle all the letters that are topologically the same as S, L, I, and M.

Which letters can be distorted to make them look like T?

Which letters can be distorted to look like O?

Which other letters can be distorted into one another?

92

Here is a Tibetan alphabet.

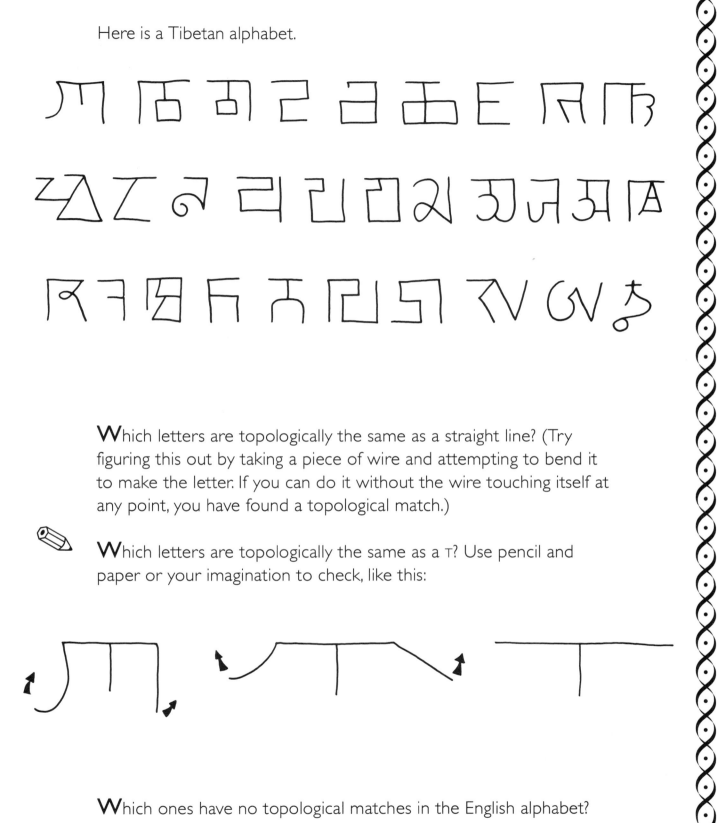

Which letters are topologically the same as a straight line? (Try figuring this out by taking a piece of wire and attempting to bend it to make the letter. If you can do it without the wire touching itself at any point, you have found a topological match.)

Which letters are topologically the same as a т? Use pencil and paper or your imagination to check, like this:

Which ones have no topological matches in the English alphabet?

Now that you've seen a lot of distortions, here's a chance to make some of your own.

 Fill in the chart. It's started for you.

ORIGINAL	DISTORTION 1	DISTORTION 2	DISTORTION 3

Here are some more drawings to distort. Try to make your distortions so elaborate that it is hard to see how each one can be twisted and stretched into the original figure. Then challenge your friends to figure out how it's done.

ORIGINAL	DISTORTION

CHAPTER 5

❧

Möbius Strips:

Some Thoughts on Doing Mathematics with a Twist

As a final twist to this book and an invitation to continue to explore the world from a mathematical point of view, here is a new challenge for you to wonder about. The techniques that you have learned and practiced in this book should come in handy when you play with this new challenge.

MÖBIUS **CHALLENGE 1**

 Begin with two identical strips of paper about eleven inches (about thirty centimeters) long and two inches (about five centimeters) wide. On one side of each strip, draw two smiling faces, one on top of the other. Then draw two scowling faces on the reverse side in similar positions.

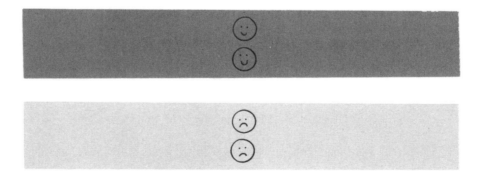

Now take one of the strips and tape the ends together, with the smiling faces out, to make a ring:

Notice that the ring has an inside surface and an outside surface, as well as two edges. If you take a colored pencil and, beginning at the smiling faces, draw a straight line around the outside of the strip, you will get back to where you started without touching the inside of the ring or either of the edges. In order to get from the smiling faces to the scowling faces, you have to cross over one of the edges.

Now take a pair of scissors and cut all the way around the ring so that the two smiling faces are on different sides of the cut.

The result is two rings, each one having a smiling face on the outside and a scowling face on the inside.

 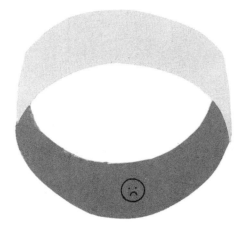

So far this may all seem very obvious, but as you've seen earlier in the book, mathematics often begins with the obvious and then, with a few simple changes, ends up with complex and unexpected results.

MÖBIUS **CHALLENGE 2**

 Take the second strip of paper with smiles and frowns on it and make a half twist in it by flipping one end over but keeping the other end still, like this:

FLIP THIS END

Now tape the ends together.

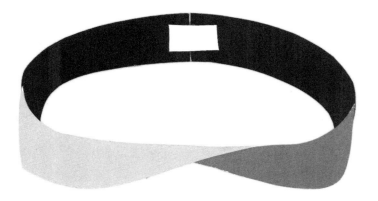

You have now created a Möbius strip. This simple and mathematically interesting model was first created and analyzed by the German mathematician Augustus Ferdinand Möbius (1790–1868). Möbius was an astronomer who used mathematics to understand the nature of space. It is possible that he developed and studied the Möbius strip while thinking about how different objects move and twist through the universe.

Using a colored pencil, draw a line beginning in the middle of the two smiling faces and around the surface of the twisted ring. Look at the differences between this ring and the ring without a twist.

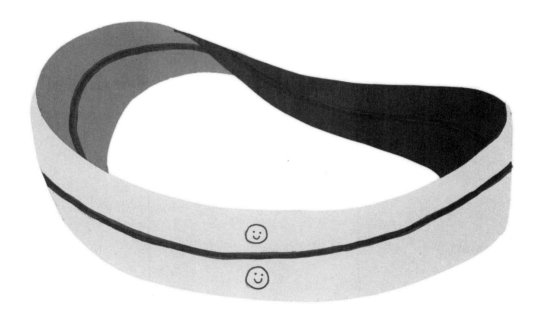

Notice that the line will move between the scowling faces as well as the happy ones in a continuous loop. There is only one surface on this twisted ring. There is no longer a front or a back, and you don't have to cross an edge to get from the smiles to the scowls.

Now, what do you expect will happen when you cut the twisted ring in half the same way you cut the first ring? Try it.

What happens?

The curious nature of the Möbius strip is not exhausted by making one simple cut. Guess what will happen if you take your new Möbius strip with the two half twists and cut around it again. Try it.

What happened?

Here are some other Möbius experiments you might like to do.

MÖBIUS **CHALLENGE 4**

 Make a much longer and wider strip of paper into a Möbius strip. Keep cutting each ring in half and see what happens.

MÖBIUS **CHALLENGE 5**

 Try cutting a Möbius strip one third of the way from one edge. Keep cutting until the cut joins up with its beginning.

What do you think the result will be?

MÖBIUS **CHALLENGE 6**

 Now make some more Möbius strips. Try cutting one of them one fifth of the way from an edge, another three fifths of the way from an edge, and so on.

What results do you find?

Twisting, cutting, drawing, figuring out patterns, and making models of mathematical ideas is one of the many ways of doing mathematics.

For almost a hundred years, the Möbius strip was considered a mathematical curiosity, a trick with no practical value. The Dutch artist M. C. Escher made this print that introduced many people to the puzzling Möbius world.

Recently, people have come up with applications of Möbius mathematics. It is thought by some physicists to be useful in thinking about the behavior of the smaller particles that make up the atom. In the practical world, almost all cartridge ribbons that are made for typewriters and computer printers are Möbius strips. This makes them last twice as long as they would if they were packaged as simple rings without a twist. Here's a perfect example of how mathematics in the mind can be transformed, in an unanticipated way, into mathematics in the world.

I hope you enjoy playing with mathematics. Keep at it. Maybe your discoveries, in addition to providing the pleasure of exercising your mind, will lead to new ways of understanding or doing things.

Answers

Chapter 1—The Curve Challenges

Page 9: A, E, G, H, I, K, M, N, O

Page 10: A, D, F, G, I, J, N, T

Page 11: inside: B, D   outside: A, C, E
inside: A, B, C   outside: D, E

Page 13: You would have to jump three hedges to get to George.
If you were with the dog, you'd have to jump five hedges to get to George.
If you were sitting at the table, you'd have to jump seven hedges to get to George.

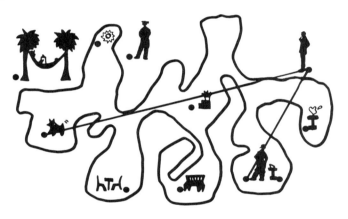

Page 14:

Getting FROM **Inside** TO **Outside**—George

FROM	TO	NUMBER OF JUMPS
Sundial	George	3
Bench	George	5
Fountain	George	1
Steps	George	3
Table	George	7
Sunny spot	George	3
Dog run	George	5

Did you notice that all of the numbers in the chart are odd numbers?

Page 15:

Getting FROM **Inside** TO **Outside**—Mary

FROM	TO	NUMBER OF JUMPS
Sundial	Mary	7
Bench	Mary	7
Fountain	Mary	7
Steps	Mary	3
Table	Mary	3
Sunny spot	Mary	1
Dog run	Mary	1

Getting FROM **Inside** TO **Outside**—Irma

FROM	TO	NUMBER OF JUMPS
Sundial	Irma	3
Bench	Irma	5
Fountain	Irma	7
Steps	Irma	1
Table	Irma	1
Sunny spot	Irma	1
Dog run	Irma	1

These numbers are also all odd.

Page 19:

Traveling FROM **Outside** TO **Outside**

FROM	TO	NUMBER OF JUMPS
You	George	2
You	Mary	10
You	Irma	8
You	Bethany	10
You	Justin	10
You	Harold	8
You	Gertrude	6
You	Spike	12
You	Puff	4

Did you observe that all of the numbers are even this time?

Did you discover the rule that when you travel from inside to outside a simple closed curve, you always cross an odd number of boundaries (hedges) and that when you travel from outside to outside, you always cross an even number?

Chapter 2—The Map Challenges

Page 26: Your map has two areas. You can color it with two colors.

Page 28: You should be able to color these maps with two colors.

Page 32: You will need two colors to color a map with one simple closed curve.

Page 34: You'll need two colors for the map with two closed curves side by side.

Page 35: You'll need two colors for the map with two intersecting closed curves:

 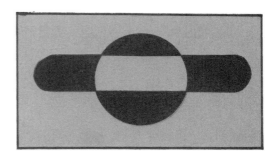

 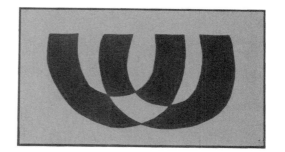

Page 37: You needed two colors.

Page 39: You should need only two colors to color these combination maps.

Page 40: Only the top left island (Tiny Island) follows the two-color rule.

Page 41: You need two colors for Tiny Island, three colors for narrow island, and four colors for Triangle Island.

Three colors.

Three colors.

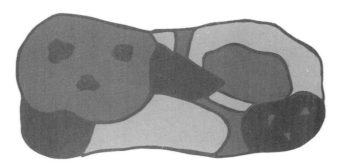

Three colors.

Four colors.

Page 43:

Four colors.

Two colors.

Three colors.

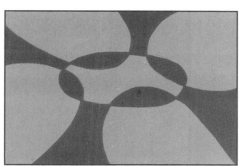
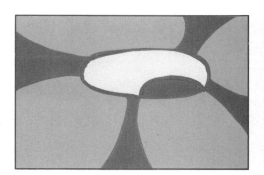

Page 46:

Three colors.

Three colors.

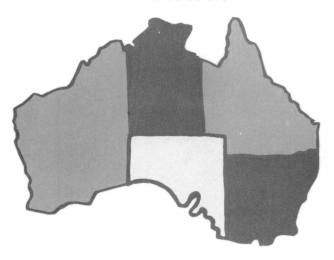

Page 47:

Four colors.

Three colors.

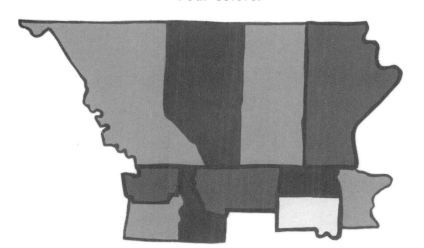
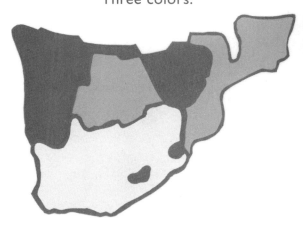

Chapter 3—The Tracing Challenges

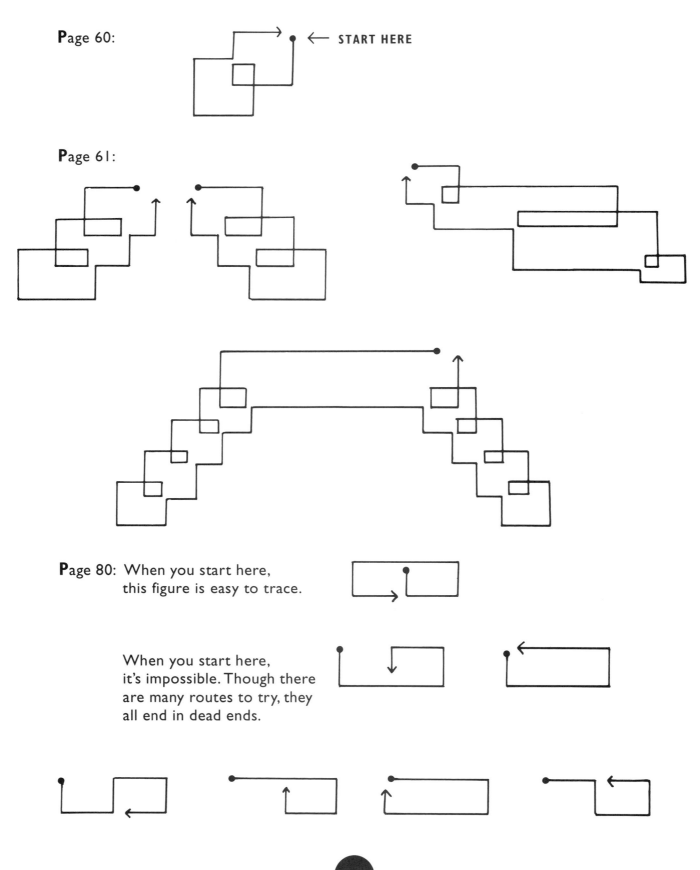

Page 60:   ← START HERE

Page 61:

Page 80: When you start here,
         this figure is easy to trace.

When you start here,
it's impossible. Though there
are many routes to try, they
all end in dead ends.

Chapter 4—The Distortion Challenges

The others have this form:

2—C is equivalent to

which cannot be transformed into

because of the way the inner two shapes are connected to the outer circle.

All of the others have this form:

4—D has this form: The rest have this form:

5—C has this form: All of the others have this form:

Page 92: The other letters that are topologically equivalent to the letters SLIM
are C, G, J, N, U, V, W, and Z.

The letters that are topologically equivalent to T are E, F, and Y.

The only letter that is topologically equivalent to O is D.

A and R are equivalent to each other. K and X are equivalent to each other.

Page 93: The following letters are equivalent to a straight line:

The following letters are equivalent to a T:

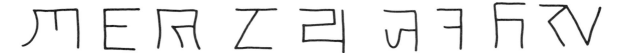

The following letters have no topological equivalents in the English language:

Chapter 5—The Möbius Challenges

These you can figure out for yourself. All answers are right, and many are unexpected.